C000202362

Glenn Miller

23 classic songs for keyboard

Published 1998

Series Editor Anna Joyce
Design & Art Direction Dominic Brookman

Music arranged & processed by Barnes Music Engraving Ltd East Sussex TN34 1HA
Cover Image Felix Man/Hulton Archive

© International Music Publications Ltd
Griffin House 161 Hammersmith Road London England W6 8BS

Reproducing this music in any form is illegal and forbidden by the Copyright, Design and Patents Act, 1988

Alice Blue Gown

Words by Joseph McCarthy / Music by Harry Tierney

Suggested Registration: Piano
Rhythm: Waltz
Tempo: ♩ = 80

In my sweet lit - tle A - lice blue

gown,_____ when I first wan - dered down in - to

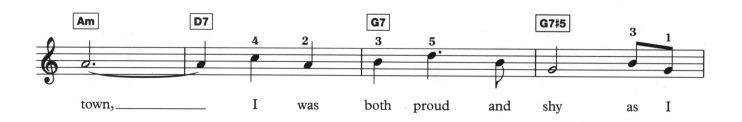

town,_____ I was both proud and shy as I

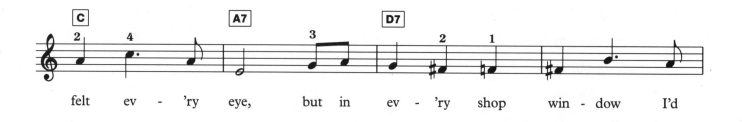

felt ev - 'ry eye, but in ev - 'ry shop win - dow I'd

'primp' pass - ing by. Then in man - ner of fash - ion I'd

© 1919 & 1998 EMI Catalogue Partnership and EMI Feist Catalog Inc, USA
Worldwide print rights controlled by Warner Bros Publications Inc/IMP Ltd and Redwood Music Ltd, London NW1 8BD

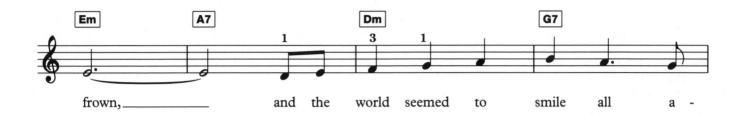

frown, _____ and the world seemed to smile all a -

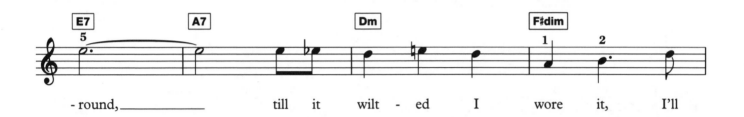

- round, _____ till it wilt - ed I wore it, I'll

al - ways a - dore it, my sweet lit - tle

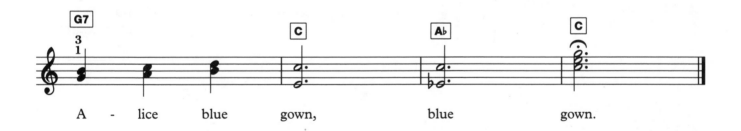

A - lice blue gown, blue gown.

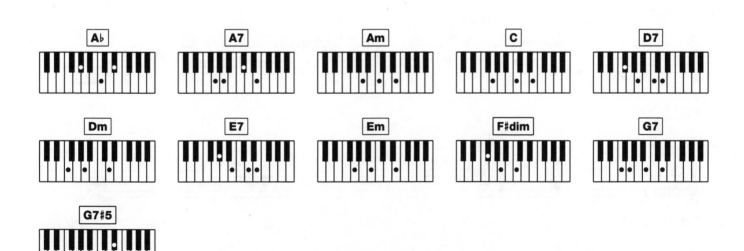

AMERICAN PATROL

Traditional

Suggested Registration: Brass
Rhythm: Swing
Tempo: ♩ = 150

© 1998 International Music Publications Limited, Woodford Green, Essex IG8 8HN

AND THE ANGELS SING

Words by Johnny Mercer / Music by Ziggie Elman

Suggested Registration: Trombone
Rhythm: Swing
Tempo: ♩ = 120

We meet_____ and the an-gels sing,_____ the an-gels

sing the sweet-est song I ev-er heard. You

speak_____ and the an-gels sing,_____ or am I breath-ing mu-sic

in-to ev-'ry word. Sud-den-ly the

set-ting is strange, I can see wa-ter and moon-light beam-ing, sil-ver waves that

break on some un-dis-cov-ered shore. Then sud-den-ly I see it all change,

© 1939 & 1998 Bregman Vocco & Conn Inc, USA

Francis Day & Hunter Ltd, London WC2H 0EA

At Last

Words by Mack Gordon / Music by Harry Warren

Suggested Registration: Vibraphone
Rhythm: Swing
Tempo: ♩ = 84

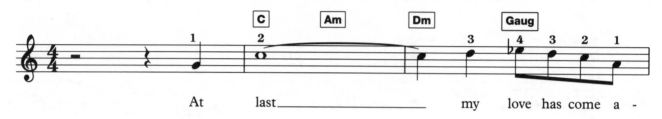

At last_____ my love has come a -

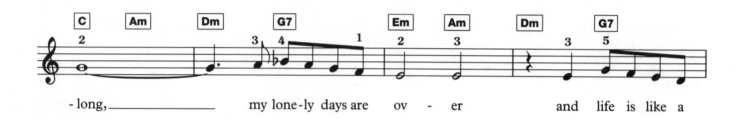

- long,_____ my lone-ly days are ov - er and life is like a

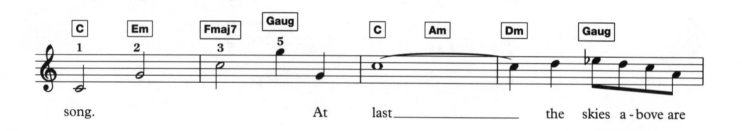

song. At last_____ the skies a - bove are

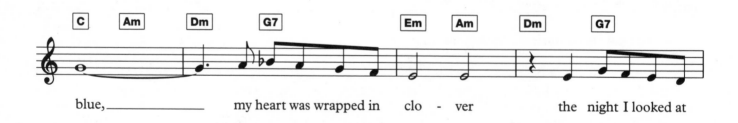

blue,_____ my heart was wrapped in clo - ver the night I looked at

you. I found a dream that I can speak to, a dream that

© 1942 & 1998 EMI Catalogue Partnership and EMI Feist Catalog Inc, USA
Worldwide print rights controlled by Warner Bros Publications Inc/IMP Ltd

I   can call my   own,   I found a   thrill   to press my

cheek to,   a   thrill I've ne - ver known.   You   smiled_____

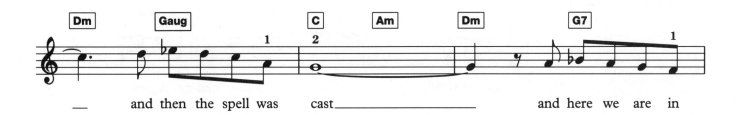

__   and then the spell was   cast_____   and here we are in

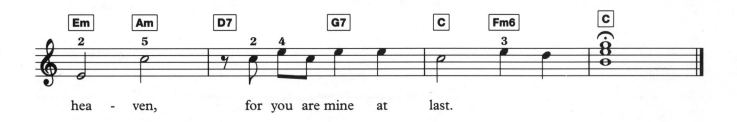

hea - ven,   for you are mine at   last.

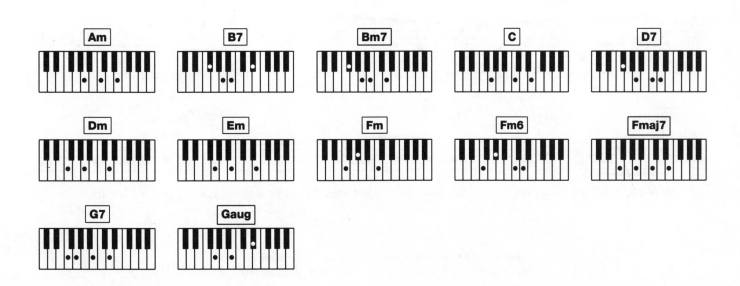

Chattanooga Choo Choo

Words by Mack Gordon / Music by Harry Warren

Suggested Registration: Clarinet
Rhythm: 8 Beat
Tempo: ♩ = 128

© 1941 & 1998 EMI Catalogue Partnership and EMI Feist Catalog Inc, USA
Worldwide print rights controlled by Warner Bros Publications Inc/IMP Ltd

Don't Sit Under The Apple Tree

Words and Music by Lew Brown, Charles Tobias and Sam Stept

Suggested Registration: Vibraphone / Jazz Guitar
Rhythm: Jazz Swing
Tempo: ♩ = 140

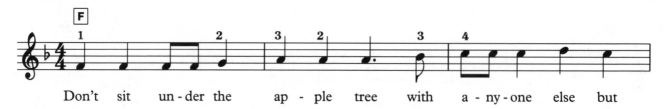

Don't sit un-der the ap-ple tree with a-ny-one else but

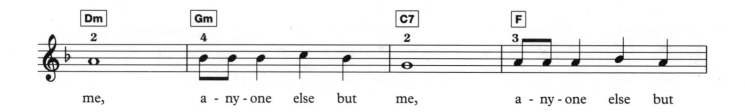

me, a-ny-one else but me, a-ny-one else but

me. No! No! No! Don't sit un-der the ap-ple tree with a-ny-one else but

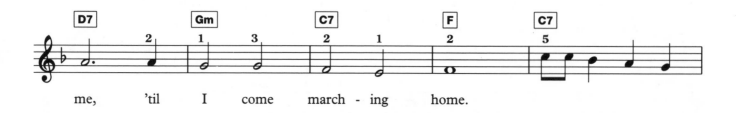

me, 'til I come march-ing home.

Don't go walk-in' down lov-er's lane with a-ny-one else but me,

a-ny-one else but me, a-ny-one else but me. No! No! No!

© 1942 & 1998 EMI Catalogue Partnership and EMI Robbins Catalog Inc, USA
Worldwide print rights controlled by Warner Bros Publications Inc/IMP Ltd,
Redwood Music Ltd, London NW1 8BD and Memory Lane Music Ltd, London WC2H 8NA

Elmer's Tune

Words and Music by Elmer Albrecht, Sammy Gallop and Dick Jurgens

Suggested Registration: Trumpet
Rhythm: Slow Rock
Tempo: ♩ = 94

Why are the stars al - ways wink - in' and blink - in' a - bove? What makes a

fel - low start think - in' of fall - in' in love?_ It's not the sea - son, the rea - son is

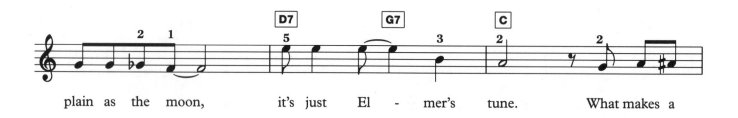

plain as the moon, it's just El - mer's tune. What makes a

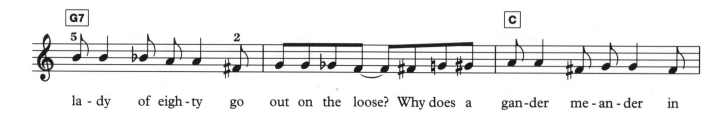

la - dy of eigh - ty go out on the loose? Why does a gan - der me - an - der in

search of a goose? What puts the kick in a chick - en, the ma - gic of June?

It's just El - mer's tune.____ Lis - ten,_ lis - ten_

© 1941 & 1998 EMI Catalogue Partnership and EMI Robbins Catalog Inc, USA
Worldwide print rights controlled by Warner Bros Publications Inc/IMP Ltd

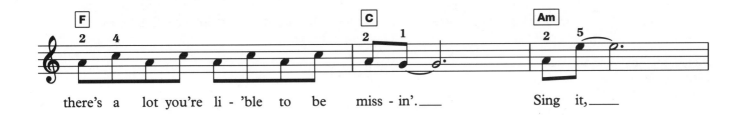

there's a lot you're li - 'ble to be miss - in'.___ Sing it,___

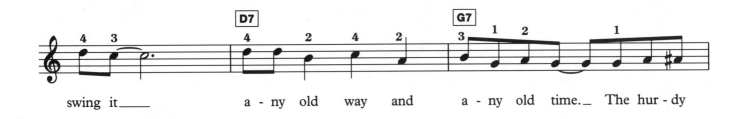

swing it___ a - ny old way and a - ny old time._ The hur - dy

gur - dies, the bird - ies, the 'cap' on the beat,___ the can - dy

ma - ker, the ba - ker, the man in the street, the ci - ty charm - er, the farm - er, the

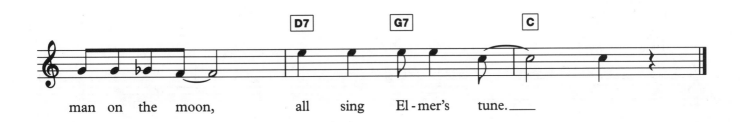

man on the moon, all sing El - mer's tune.___

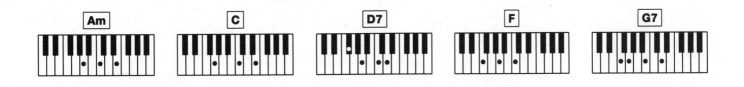

Hear My Song, Violetta

Original Words by Othmar Klose, English Words by Harry S Pepper / Music by Othmar Klose and Rudolf Luckesch

Suggested Registration: Violin
Rhythm: Tango
Tempo: ♩ = 110

© 1936 & 1998 Adopho Robischek Musikverlag, Austria
Dix Ltd, London WC2H 0EA

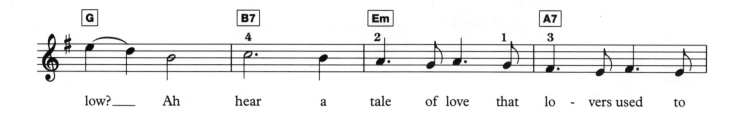

low?___ Ah hear a tale of love that lo - vers used to

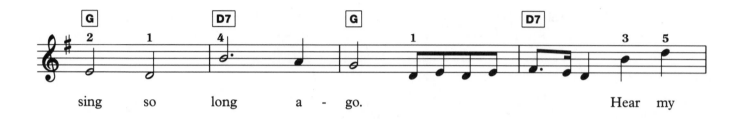

sing so long a - go. Hear my

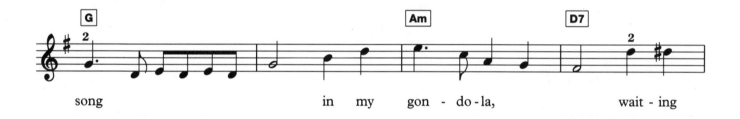

song in my gon - do - la, wait - ing

on the old lag - oon.

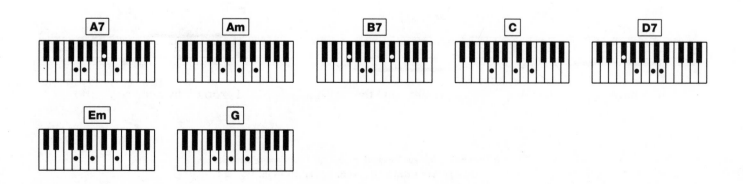

I Know Why And So Do You

Words by Mack Gordon / Music by Harry Warren

Suggested Registration: Clarinet
Rhythm: Swing
Tempo: ♩ = 80

Why do rob-ins sing in De - cem - ber, long be -fore the spring -time is

due, and e - ven though it's snow-ing, vi - o -lets are grow-ing?

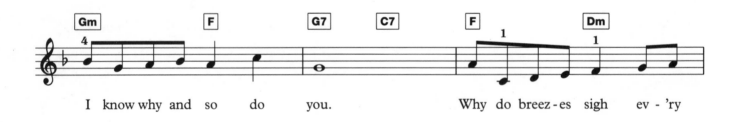

I know why and so do you. Why do breez-es sigh ev - 'ry

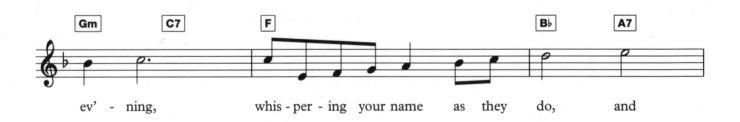

ev' - ning, whis -per - ing your name as they do, and

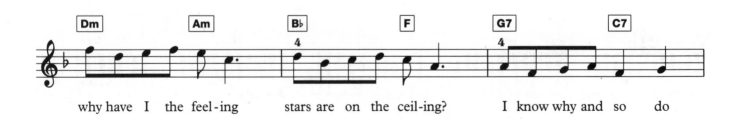

why have I the feel-ing stars are on the ceil-ing? I know why and so do

© 1941 & 1998 EMI Catalogue Partnership and EMI Feist Catalog Inc, USA
Worldwide print rights controlled by Warner Bros Publications Inc/IMP Ltd

In The Mood

Words and Music by Joe Garland

Suggested Registration: Tenor Saxophone
Rhythm: Swing
Tempo: ♩ = 120

Who's the liv-in' dol-ly with the beau-ti-ful eyes? What a pair o' lips, I'd like to

try 'em for size._ I'll just tell her, 'Ba-by, won't you swing it with me?'_

Hope she tells me may-be, what a wing it will be._ So I said po-lite-ly, 'Dar-lin',

may I in-trude?' She said, 'Don't keep me wait-ing when I'm in the mood.'

First I held her light-ly, and we start-ed to dance, then I held her tight-ly, what a

dream-y ro-mance, and I said, 'Hey ba-by, it's a quart-er to three,

© 1939 & 1998 Shapiro Bernstein & Co Inc, USA

Peter Maurice Music Co Ltd, London WC2H 0EA

It Happened In Sun Valley

Words by Mack Gordon / Music by Harry Warren

Suggested Registration: Jazz Guitar
Rhythm: Cha-Cha
Tempo: ♩ = 116

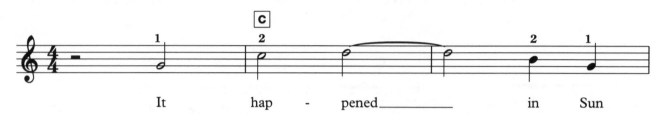

It   hap - pened _____ in Sun

Val - ley _____ not so ve - ry _____ long a -

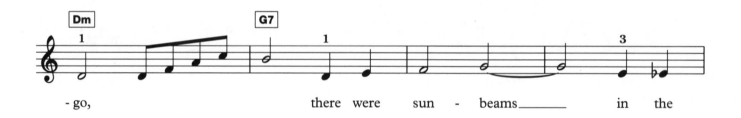

- go,   there were sun - beams _____ in the

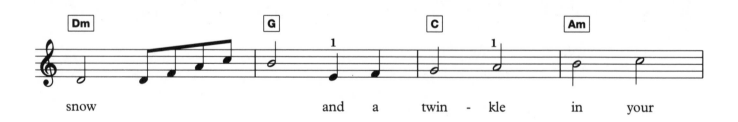

snow   and a twin - kle in your

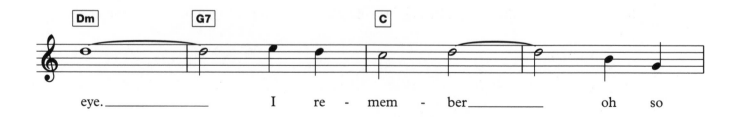

eye. _____ I re - mem - ber _____ oh so

© 1941 & 1998 EMI Catalogue Partnership and EMI Feist Catalog Inc, USA
Worldwide print rights controlled by Warner Bros Publications Inc/IMP Ltd

clear - ly_____ that you near - ly_____ passed me

by, then it hap - pened in Sun

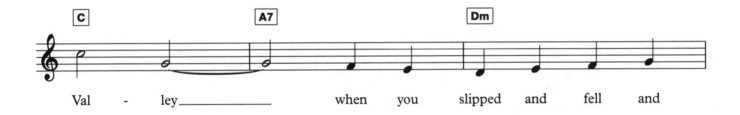

Val - ley_____ when you slipped and fell and

so did I.

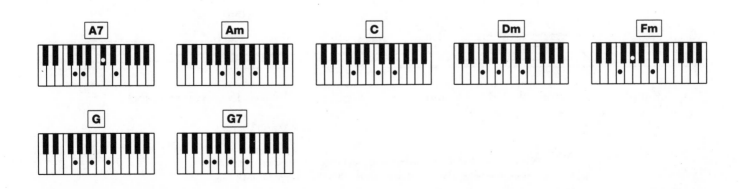

Johnson Rag

Words by Jack Lawrence / Music by Guy Hall and Henry Kleinkauf

Suggested Registration: Piano
Rhythm: Swing
Tempo: ♩ = 142

Hep!   Hep!_____ There goes the   John - son rag.___ Hoy!

Hoy!_____ There goes the   lat - est rag.___ Ho!   Ho!_____ It real - ly

is - n't a gag.___ Hep!   Hep!_____ There goes the   John - son rag.___ Jump!

Jump!_____ Don't let your   left   foot drag.___ Jeep!   Jeep!_____ It's like a

game   of tag.___ Juke!   Juke!_____ It's e - ven   good for a   stag.___ Jump!

Jump!_____ And do the   John - son rag.___   If   you're feel - in'

© 1940 & 1998 EMI Catalogue Partnership and EMI Robbins Catalog Inc, USA
Worldwide print rights controlled by Warner Bros Publications Inc/IMP Ltd

25

in the groove it sends you out of the world.___

Fun - ny how it makes you move I don't want to coax,_ but

don't be a 'mokes'. Zig! Zig!_____ Then add a Zig! Zig! Sag!_ Zoop!

Zoop!_____ Just let your should - ers wag._ Zoom! Zoom!_____ And now it's

right in the bag._ Get hep, and get hap - py with the John - son rag._

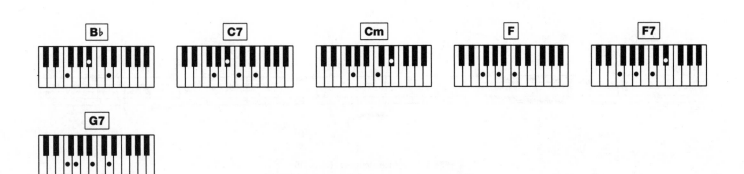

King Porter Stomp

Music by Ferd 'Jelly Roll' Morton, Arranged by Sonny Burke and Sid Robin

Suggested Registration: Honky Tonk Piano
Rhythm: Swing
Tempo: ♩ = 120

© 1924 & 1998 Melrose Music Corp, USA
Herman Darewski Music Pub Co, London WC2H 0EA

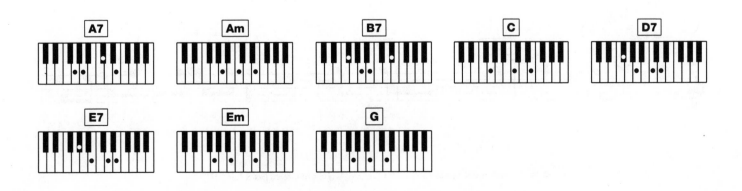

27

LITTLE BROWN JUG

Music by R A Eastburn

Suggested Registration: Saxophone
Rhythm: Swing
Tempo: ♩ = 114

© 1998 International Music Publications Limited, Woodford Green, Essex IG8 8HN

Moonlight Serenade

Words by Mitchell Parish / Music by Glenn Miller

Suggested Registration: Saxophone
Rhythm: Slow Swing
Tempo: ♩ = 72

© 1939 & 1998 EMI Catalogue Partnership and EMI Robbins Catalog Inc, USA
Worldwide print rights controlled by Warner Bros Publications Inc/IMP Ltd

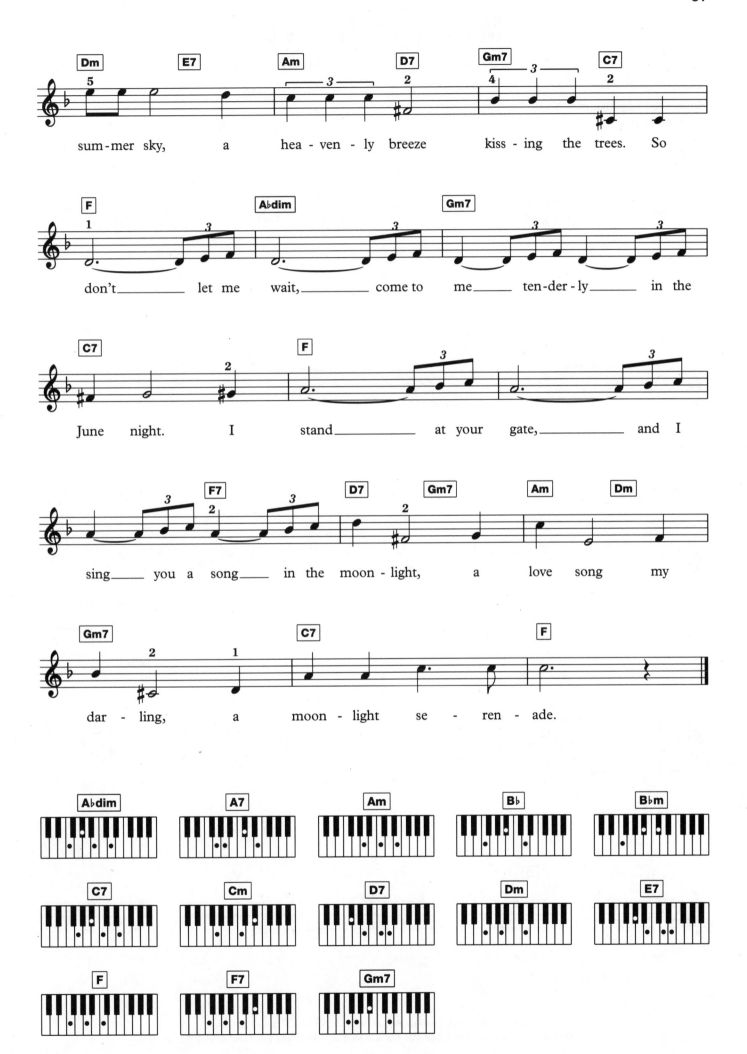

My Blue Heaven

Words by George Whiting / Music by Walter Donaldson

Suggested Registration: Muted Trumpet
Rhythm: Swing
Tempo: ♩ = 154

When whip-poor-wills

call _____ and ev-'ning is nigh, _____ I hur - ry to

my blue hea - ven. A turn to the

right, _____ a lit - tle white light _____ will lead you to

my blue hea - ven. You'll see a

© 1927 & 1998 EMI Catalogue Partnership and EMI Feist Catalog Inc, USA
EMI Music Publishing Ltd, London WC2H 0EA and Memory Lane Music Ltd, London WC2H 8NA

smil - ing face, a fire - place, a co - zy room,_____ a

lit - tle nest that's nest - led where the ro - ses bloom. Just Mol-lie and

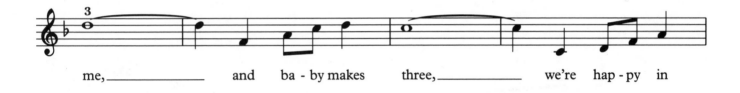

me,_____ and ba - by makes three,_____ we're hap - py in

my blue hea - ven._____

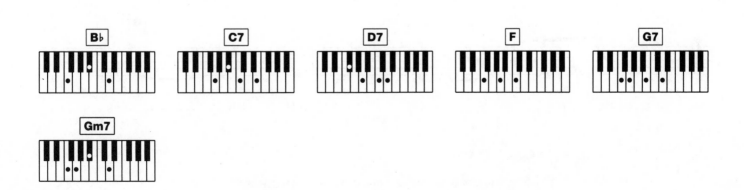

My Guy's Come Back

Words by Ray McKinley / Music by Mel Powell

Suggested Registration: Trumpet
Rhythm: Jazz Swing
Tempo: ♩ = 140

Some-thin's cook-in' that-'ll rate an o - va-tion, will you note that I am in a

state of e - la-tion, won't you call the press in, 'cos I've got a quo - ta-tion, and I'll

tell the na-tion that my guy's come back. No more

blues for me, no, no more, no more,

— just good

© 1945 & 1998 Peter Maurice Music Co Ltd, London WC2H 0EA

news for me,＿＿＿ just good news＿＿＿ in store.

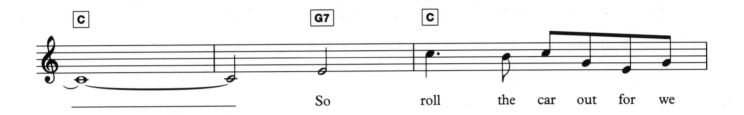

＿＿＿＿＿ So roll the car out for we

got-ta get mov-in', let us have a star out for my guy is a-prov-in' ev-'ry

time, we're step-pin' out we real-ly get groov-in', and the life's im-prov-in' for my

guy's come back.＿

Pennsylvania 6-5000

Words by Carl Sigman / Music by Jerry Gray

Suggested Registration: Brass
Rhythm: Swing
Tempo: ♩ = 128

Num-bers I've got by the doz - en, ___ ev - 'ry-one's un-cle and

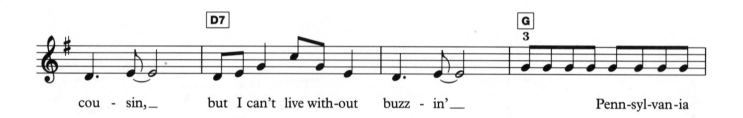

cou - sin, ___ but I can't live with-out buzz - in' ___ Penn-syl-van-ia

six, five thous-and. I've got a sweet-ie I know there, ___

some - one who sets me a - glow there, ___ gives me the sweet-est 'hel -

- lo there' Penn-syl-van-ia six, five thous-and. We don't say 'How

© 1940 & 1998 EMI Catalogue Partnership and EMI Robbins Catalog Inc, USA
Worldwide print rights controlled by Warner Bros Publications Inc/IMP Ltd

37

are you',____ and ve - ry sel - dom ask____ what's new, in -

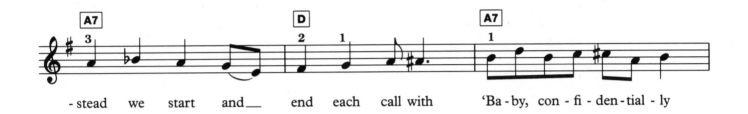

- stead we start and____ end each call with 'Ba - by, con - fi - den - tial - ly

I love you.' May-be it sounds a bit fun - ny____ when I'm a - way from my

hon - ey,____ here's what I'd do with my mon - ey____

Penn-syl-van - ia six, five thou - sand. Ooh! Ooh!

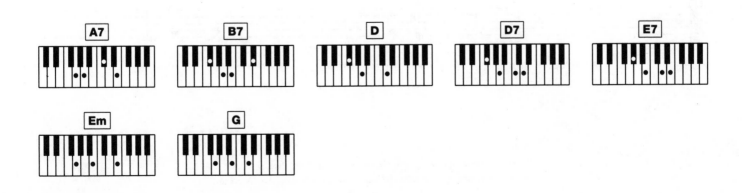

Running Wild

Words by Joe Gray and Leo Wood / Music by Arthur Harrington Gibbs

Suggested Registration: Brass
Rhythm: Swing
Tempo: ♩ = 150

Run-ning wild, _____ lost con - trol, _____

run-ning wild, _____ migh - ty bold, _____

feel - ing gay, _____ reck-less too. _____

Care-free mind ___ all the time, _____ ne - ver blue, _____

© 1922 & 1998 EMI Catalogue Partnership and EMI Feist Catalog Inc, USA
Worldwide print rights controlled by Warner Bros Publications Inc/IMP Ltd

al - way's goin', ___ don't know where, ___

al - way's showin' ___ I don't care. ___

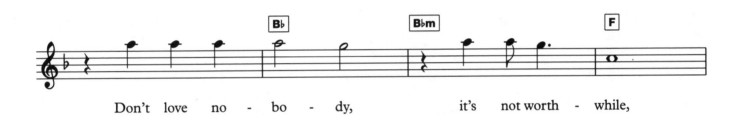

Don't love no - bo - dy, it's not worth - while,

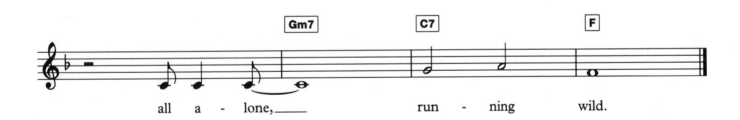

all a - lone, ___ run - ning wild.

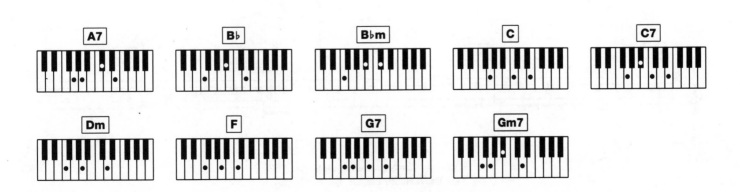

St Louis Blues

Music by W C Handy

Suggested Registration: Brass
Rhythm: Shuffle or Swing
Tempo: ♩ = 98

© 1914 & 1998 Handy Brothers Music Co Inc, USA
Francis Day & Hunter Ltd, London WC2H 0EA

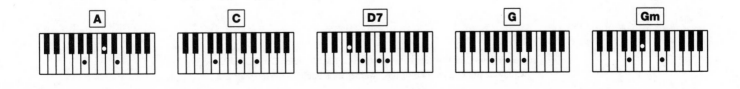

Stairway To The Stars

Words by Mitchell Parish / Music by Matty Malneck and Frank Signorelli

Suggested Registration: Electric Piano
Rhythm: Swing
Tempo: ♩ = 80

Let's build a stair-way to the stars, and climb that

stair - way to the stars, with love be - side us just

like a beau - ti - ful song.

We'll hear the sound of vi - o - lins, out yon - der

where the blue be -gins, the moon will guide us, as we go drift - ing a -

- long. Can't we sail a - way

© 1939 & 1998 EMI Catalogue Partnership and EMI Robbins Catalog Inc, USA
Worldwide print rights controlled by Warner Bros Publications Inc/IMP Ltd

Sunrise Serenade

Words by Jack Lawrence / Music by Frankie Carle

Suggested Registration: Vibraphone
Rhythm: Slow Rock
Tempo: ♩ = 76

Good morn-in', good morn-in' you sleep-y head, it's

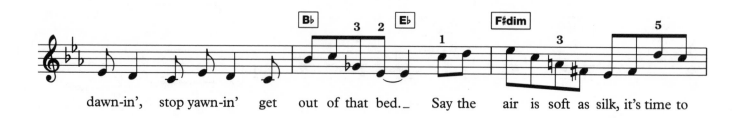

dawn-in', stop yawn-in' get out of that bed.__ Say the air is soft as silk, it's time to

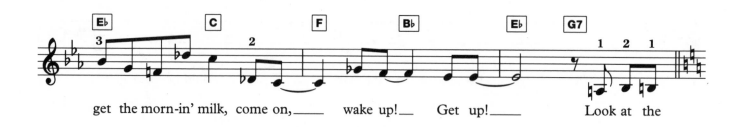

get the morn-in' milk, come on,___ wake up!__ Get up!___ Look at the

grass, sil-ver in the sun, hea-vy with the dew, look at the

buds, you can al-most see how they're break-in' thro'._____ Look at the

© 1938 Jewel Music Publishing Co Inc, USA
Jewel Music Pub Co Inc, London WC2H 8NA

birds feed - in' all their young in the sy - ca - mores, but you

bet - ter get on with your morn - in' chores._____ Just take a

breath of that new - mown hay and the su - gar cane,_____ looks like to -

- night there should be a moon down in lov - ers' lane. There you

go, day dream-ing when it's time that you o-beyed that sun - rise se - ren - ade.

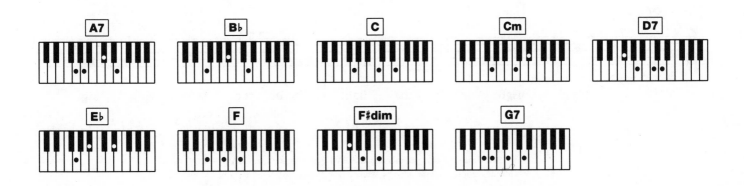

Wonderful One

Words by Dorothy Terriss / Music by Paul Whiteman, Ferde Grofé and Marshall Neilan

Suggested Registration: Strings
Rhythm: Waltz
Tempo: ♩ = 90

My won - der - ful one, when - ev - er I'm

dream - ing 'tis love - light a gleam - ing I see.

My won - der - ful one, to my heart I would

fold you, for - ev - er to hold you to___ me.

Though bright be the light of the stars shin - ing

© 1922 EMI Catalogue Partnership and EMI Feist Catalog Inc, USA
Worldwide print rights controlled by Warner Bros Publications Inc/IMP Ltd

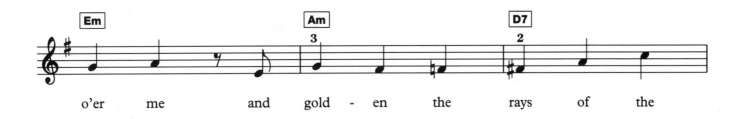

o'er me and gold - en the rays of the

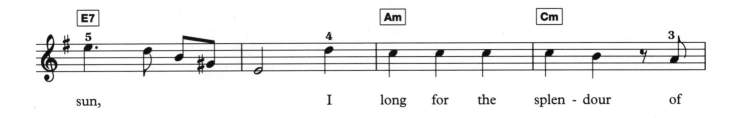

sun, I long for the splen - dour of

eyes true and ten - der, my won - der - ful,

won - der - ful one.

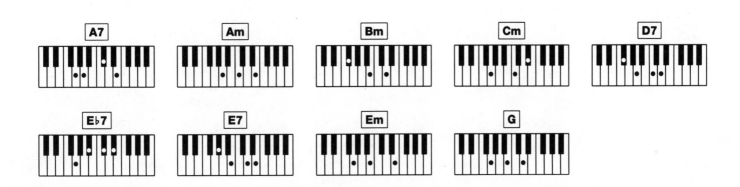

Printed and bound in Great Britain